*F*oreword

Dear Friends:

We didn't plan to write a book.

We are six women who share a love of quilting and became friends through our local quilt club. When round-robin quilts were a new idea, we decided to give it a try. Our first project was so much fun: keeping secrets about what had just been added, collaborating on what to do next, inspiring and motivating each other, and stretching our creativity. We were delighted with the results of our first project so we decided to do another.

Our second round-robin was completely different from the first. Each of us began a story and created an accompanying quilt background. The story quilts made the rounds to each person who continued the story and embellished the quilt. While a more challenging task than our first round-robin, it was very enjoyable and our friendships grew.

Together we have completed four round-robins and after finishing each one, we showed our work to our quilt club. Soon other guilds began inviting us to share our experiences and quilts. After the presentations we were often asked, "When are you going to write a book?" The thought intrigued us and we accepted the challenge.

This book is a compilation of the stories and quilts from our second round-robin. We hope you enjoy our "story quilts" and that they inspire you to accept new challenges and explore your creativity.

© 2002 Six Friends
All rights reserved. No part of this book may be reproduced in any form without permission from the authors.

Published in the USA

Books and patterns may be ordered from the following address/s:

Six Friends
9332 Rhoy Avenue
Chaska, MN 55318

e-mail: <jgoet@worldnet.att.net>

To Kathy,
Thank you for all your help.
Love, Mom

The Clothesline
& Other Quilt Stories

By:
Six Friends

Joan Goetteman   Dianne Prentice
Jackie Olmstead   Vicky Ress
Chris Peterson   Audree Sells

Table of Contents

Circus Time 7

The Front Porch 15

The Clothesline 23

Grandma's Attic 33

The Garden Gate 43

Night Magic 51

Acknowledgments 60

Follow your dreams! That's the advice the "wise ones" give. I often wonder where I would be had I followed the yellow brick road.

Under the big top is where I would start, with all the animals and trainers, acrobats and stars. Oh, what fun I would have watching elephants fly!

I might have been the star of the show on a tightrope or an animal trainer who taught the animals how to jump through hoops. The sounds, the smells, the glitter of the big top are calling me now.

Or, maybe I would be the lead clown—the master of fun and exaggeration. I could make people laugh and forget their troubles.

How could I resist the temptation to be the Great Wizard? I would fire up my balloon and fulfill the wish of anyone who has ever wanted to float through the sky.

Stop! Stop! How can anyone pick one favorite part of the circus? It's impossible! I love it all: the noise and excitement, the laughter and music, the sights, the smells, the animals, the popcorn, and the peanuts. I want it all, and so I will have it—every time I sit in the stands and watch the clowns play tricks on each other and me.

23" X 40" Jackie's Quilt

The Front Porch

During the long Minnesota winter, my thoughts often drift to warmer days, front porches, and my flowers.

I close my eyes and imagine bees buzzing, working the hollyhocks.

Everywhere I look, I see or smell the flowers. Even from inside the house, I look out and see the flowers growing in the old wicker planter. As ugly as that old planter is, it looks beautiful filled with flowers. I love that old thing. If not for that planter. . . .

I never would have found the old wicker rocking chair stashed in the dark corner of the musty basement at the home having the estate sale. The chair looked beyond repair, but I knew it could be saved. I had the perfect spot for it on the front porch. This chair would be my special place for quilting, reading, or just watching my flowers grow.

The old mother cat purred at the foot of the rocker, waiting for me to sit and sew. But it was Saturday. I had just watered the big pot in the corner and stopped to admire the cone-shaped pine in the front yard

when my neighbor called from the white frame house beyond the hollyhocks. . .

"Have you seen the blue jays and the cardinals yet?" she asked. Ahh! Summer was finally here!

The Front Porch

23" X 22"

Vicky's Quilt

The Clothesline

It was a beautiful spring morning on the farm. The daffodils were in full bloom and the tulips had just started to show their colors. Sitting on her front porch sipping her morning coffee, Anna thought, "What a perfect day to air out my quilts on the clothesline!"

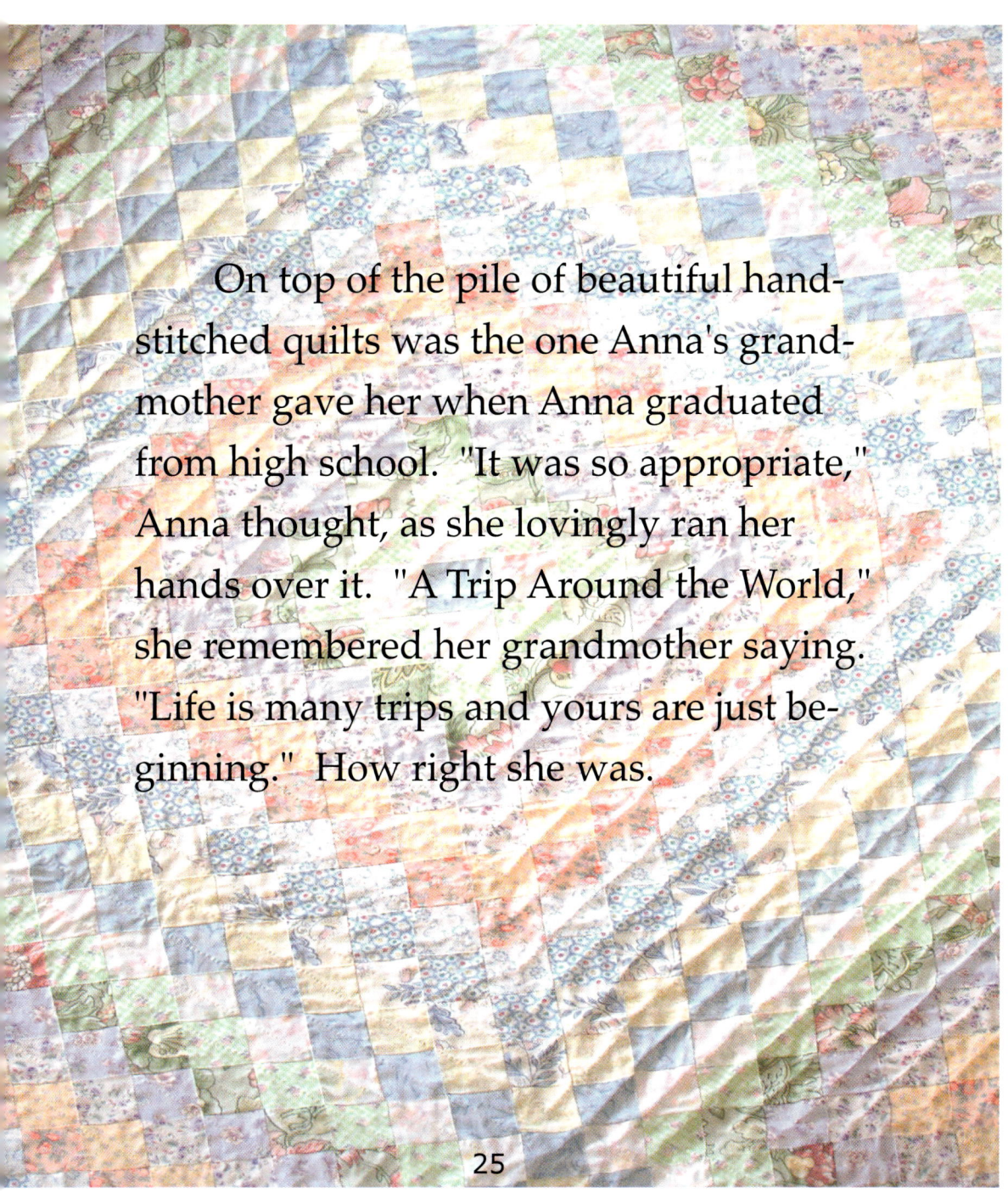

    On top of the pile of beautiful hand-stitched quilts was the one Anna's grandmother gave her when Anna graduated from high school. "It was so appropriate," Anna thought, as she lovingly ran her hands over it. "A Trip Around the World," she remembered her grandmother saying. "Life is many trips and yours are just beginning." How right she was.

The next quilt on the pile brought back fond memories of friendship and community. This was the first one Anna had quilted with her neighbors.
They all arrived early, the men to raise the barn and the women to prepare the food as quickly as possible, so they could get to their favorite activities—talking and quilting.

 When the sun finally began to set and everyone was heading home, the barn was raised and Anna's beautiful Maple Leaf quilt was finished. She knew each stitch and cherished the friends who put them there.

Anna loved the farm. As she hung her Dutchman's Puzzle quilt, she remembered her Dutch ancestors who settled the land. She was glad they had come here. She loved the change of the seasons and the accompanying changes in the rhythms of life on the farm.

Spring was her favorite time, full of new beginnings: the flowers and trees coming to life, the crops being sown and the farm animals giving birth. She enjoyed tending her gardens and watching things grow throughout the summer. The fall harvest gave a feeling of satisfaction from having completed the cycle. Winter was special because it brought a well-deserved rest and allowed her time to quilt.

She finished the Lone Star quilt this past winter. Her mother had taught her how to make it. Anna loved the colorful fabrics. She would give this quilt to her daughter, just as her mother had given quilts to her.

What a wonderful day to sit and enjoy the weather. Most of the spring-cleaning was finished, the garden was planted and beginning to sprout. Who could want anything more? Life was good.

   Looking over the land, Anna began dreaming of her next quilt. Perhaps it would have farm animals. It could have cows, chickens, pigs, the mare and her colt, and Jeb, the farm dog. Patty, Anna's golden retriever, would have a special place on it, just as she had a special place in Anna's heart. The rich browns of the freshly turned soil and the glorious greens of the rolling hills could be the quilt's backdrop.

"Wouldn't it be fun to include hot air balloons floating in the distance?" pondered Anna. She could even include the Jacob farm and ol' Peter plowing with his horses. Yes, this would be a grand quilt!

As Anna pictured her favorite things: her gardens, her flowers along the porch, and her quilts blowing in the wind, she knew this would be her life quilt. Anna was excited! She would choose her fabrics carefully.

She decided to call her friends and ask them to share some fabrics. They would be part of her quilt, adding color, charm, and interest, just as they did in her life. Anna was anxious to begin her new quilt. It felt as if it was already half finished.

The Clothesline

45" X 47"

Chris's Quilt

Grandma's Attic

Some of my fondest childhood memories include summers spent at Grandma and Grandpa Johnson's farm near Grantsburg, Wisconsin. I was seven years old and my sister Cheryl was five, the first summer we spent with them.

We lived on a farm ourselves, but it was fun helping our grandparents with the chores. We helped Grandpa feed the calves and gathered eggs with Grandma, played with the new baby kittens, and picked strawberries from the garden. On rainy days we played inside and explored the attic.

The attic was one big room, as big as the entire house, with windows on each end and a vaulted ceiling. The walls were unpainted and the floor was made of wooden planks. There were all kinds of treasures in the attic, wonderful things to look at and touch. If we were very careful, we could play with them. I especially loved the old trunk, where I would find things to play make-believe.

Cheryl would claim her spot on the musty, old, blue rug and drag out the dollhouse that Grandpa made for Mama when she was eight. Grandma kept it after Mama married Papa. When Mama had her  babies, Grandma thought it best to keep the dollhouse in her attic so the young ones wouldn't swallow the small objects. I think Cheryl liked the dollhouse because it had a mama and papa doll and only two children.

Of course, Cheryl was the oldest child in the dollhouse family. She decided the boy doll was actually a girl in pants with a very short haircut. She named her Joan. The dollhouse family also included Blacky, the black dog, and Whitey, the white cat. All day she was content to play on that old rug with her perfect family. As for me, I had more important play to work at.

Standing so quietly and proudly in the corner was Grandma's old dress-form, my "lady in waiting." She never made a sound, but I carried on a conversation with her anyway and made believe her answers were so funny and witty that I would get to giggling.

She loved to get all dressed up and I had so much fun digging through the old trunk and boxes around her, finding just the right outfit for that day. Each day was an adventure.

We never knew if we would end up at a church social, a picnic in the park, or enjoy a quiet afternoon tea— just the two of us.

Besides the dress-up clothes, the trunk contained toys my grandma had saved. Some of them were from her childhood. The stuffed animals were Mama's. She took good care of them. We loved the old books, and sometimes Grandma came up to the attic to read to us. We took some wild rides on the old stick horse, too.

Sometimes when Grandma was in her best mood, she would open her hatboxes and let us try on her precious old hats. They made us feel so grown-up. Every now and then she would open the very bottom box containing my great-grandma's hat. We could only look at that hat, but I loved it, probably because that was when Grandma would tell me how much I resembled my great-grandma.

Everyone says I look and act like my great-grandma: the round face, long hair, the quiet manners, and the mischievous sense of humor. Her portrait hangs in the attic, and I spent hours looking at it trying to see the resemblance.

One of our favorite games to play at Grandma's house was hide and seek. I liked to hide in the old wardrobe up in the attic. Surrounded by the clothes, I would think about all the stories Grandma and Grandpa told about the olden days. I wish I had lived back then too, so I could go on sleigh rides and fetch water.

In the evening I would ask Grandma to bring down the kerosene lantern. We'd sit in its soft glow while Grandma and Grandpa told stories about Mama when she was young and about their childhood and when they were courting.

Once in awhile something I recognized from the attic appeared in their stories. It wasn't until I was older that I realized the attic wasn't just a fun place where I could let my imagination soar; it was a storehouse of treasured memories for my family.

40

Grandma's Attic

22" X 21"

Joan's Quilt

The Garden Gate

Rebekah couldn't wait. It had been years since she had worked with her grandmother in the garden, the place that brought peace and joy to her soul. She had returned to visit and to replenish her spirit. With great anticipation, she donned her garden hat, took a deep breath, and headed for the garden gate.

As she approached, Rebekah was struck anew by the beauty of the garden.

She recognized many of the flowers in bloom. The delicious smells and the feel of the stones under her feet carried her back in time.

When Rebekah was very young, her grandmother taught her the names of the flowers: the daffodil and larkspur, the coral bells and sweet-smelling alyssum, and of course, the rose. But, her favorite was the purple coneflower.

Just on the other side of the fence was the big old oak tree. Her grandmother kissed her first beau under that tree. However, Rebekah didn't think it was Granddad. There were initials carved in the tree—R.B. + J.T. She asked who J.T. was. Grandmother smiled, told her to hop on the swing, and gave her a giant push. She flew through the air—going up, up, up over the garden fence. It was the most pleasant thing.

47

The sun beat down as Rebekah filled the watering can and gave the flowers along the stone path a cool, refreshing drink. It had been a long, hot summer and Mother Nature needed a helping hand with the watering. Even the birdbath had gone dry, so Rebekah filled it and then sat down on the marble bench to watch the birds splash and play. She wondered if there could be a more perfect spot on earth.

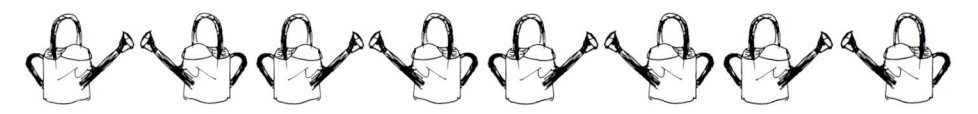

The Garden Gate

32" X 38"

Dianne's Quilt

Night Magic

Rachel couldn't fall asleep; something was keeping her awake. She got up and looked out her bedroom window. A glorious silver moon hung over the dark world below.

In the moonlight, Rachel saw the wings of fairies as they danced and played and sprinkled magic dust. They seemed to hover just for a moment above her window box, enticing her to come out and play.

The world outside was filled with wonder. Magical visions seemed to come to life before Rachel's eyes.

The lights twinkled in the distance and she could hear sounds so clearly. She heard a dog bark and the clock tower "bong". Some children were still playing in the moonlight and she heard the fluttering of wings. Were these really fairies or was it something else?

Rachel recognized the fluttering sound and her heart skipped a beat. Yes! It was her friend, Stratus, the magical dragon. Stratus stood guard over the cumulus castle and protected Fairy Princess Racheline from the bats and the beast.

Oh, what a nasty fellow that beast Mortimus was! He was the terror of Rachel's mystical kingdom. Tonight he was trying his hardest to scare those dainty fairies into never coming around his neighborhood again. They were just too cute for his fancy.

Wouldn't you know, Stratus had to show up and ruin his party. The two of them could have been such good friends and ruled the kingdom together. But no-o-o-o, Stratus was Rachel's hero and would do anything to keep her from harm.

Mortimus was in a particularly bad mood this evening. Those pesky bats were giving him a headache. They were caught in his fur and all their fluttering was getting on his nerves. To top it off, a fog was moving in. If he didn't move fast, it would be too thick to see anything and his plan to take over the kingdom would fail. Suddenly, from out of the dark sky came a burst of blinding light! It was Mortimus' worst fear—shooting stars. For a monster like him, it meant doom. He had to get back to his cave immediately, or he would perish from the brilliant display of flashing colors.

With one last helpless glance, he turned away from the castle and the fairies and hurried off to the safety of his den, grumbling as he went. Rachel held her breath as she watched the beast retreat into the night. She knew he would be back again another night, just as he always promised.

At last all was quiet again. The fairies flew off to rest in the vines, their magic dust settling to the ground. Stratus put out his fire and the stars returned to their orbits, twinkling as they went. As the clock tower chimed, Rachel closed her eyes and sighed.

All was safe and it was time to sleep.

Night Magic

30" X 24"

Audree's Quilt

Acknowledgments

We give grateful thanks to:
- all the quilters who appreciate our work and continue to offer us encouragement;
- Sue Freese (Jackie's friend) who made our "book idea" happen by typing the original draft and making all those photos slide into place;
- Maureen Harlander and Barbara Swenson (Vicky's faculty friends from the English department) for reading our manuscript with a sharp eye;
- Suzanne Thiesfeld (Audree's daughter) for sketching a plan to use real-life inspirational photos, artwork and text arrangement;
- Audree Sells for original watercolor designs and Rachel Thiesfeld, age 8, for her drawings of the fanciful fairy, the mean monster, and the dandy dragon;
- Kathryn Baker (Audree's daughter) for her patience—taking photos again and again, until they were perfect;
- Bruce Goetteman (Joan's husband) for hours of tireless editing and page-layout revisions, finally arriving at the finished product.

Finally, a special thank you to our families for their patience with our creative chaos so that we can stretch in new directions.

L to R: Audree Sells, Joan Goetteman, Chris Peterson, Dianne Prentice, Vicky Ress, Jackie Olmstead